# More Adventures of the Superkids

## A Super Way to Learn

by Pleasant T. Rowland

Shirleyann Costigan, Anne Martin, Donna Staples
contributing writers

▲ Addison-Wesley Publishing Company

Menlo Park, California • Reading, Massachusetts
London • Amsterdam • Don Mills, Ontario • Sydney

Loretta Lustig, Meryl Henderson, Kristine Bollinger
illustrators

Martha Lehtola, designer

1987 printing
Copyright © 1982, 1979 by Addison-Wesley Publishing Company, Inc. All Rights Reserved.
No part of this publication may be reproduced, stored in a retrieval system, or transmitted, in any
form or by any means, electronic, mechanical, photocopying, recording, or otherwise, without the
prior written permission of the publisher.
Printed in the United States of America. Published simultaneously in Canada.

ISBN 0-201-21750-3    BCDEFG-VH-8987

# Table of Contents

# Chapter 1
## In Case of Rain 6

| | | | |
|---|---|---|---|
| by | chilly | muddy | clay |
| dry | drizzly | nifty | day |
| my | easy | nippy | lay |
| try | frizzy | plenty | play |
| | frosty | pretty | spray |
| | funny | rainy | stay |
| | happy | really | way |
| | hungry | sleepy | |
| | Icky | very | |
| | Lily | windy | |
| | messy | yukky | |

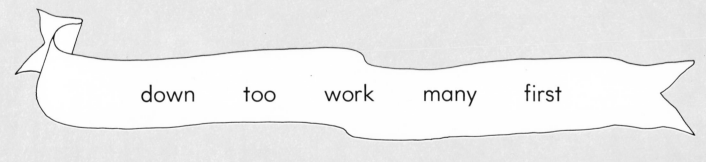

down     too     work     many     first

paper

# In Case of Rain

It was a very rainy day. It was
so wet that the Superkids had to
play in the bus. So, they made
up games and projects to
do inside. Read about the many
things they made up to do. Pick the
game or project you like best,
and work on it the next time it is
drizzly,
chilly,
windy,
rainy,
nippy,
frosty,
muddy,
or just plain yukky!

Rainy Day Projects
Super Plans
From Superkids' Brains

# Make a Leaf Print
## by Lily and Hot Rod

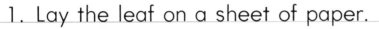

Things You Need:

a leaf        a small brush

a flat stick    a sheet of paper

some paint—tempera paint will work best

1. Lay the leaf on a sheet of paper.
2. Dip the brush in the paint.
3. Take the brush in one hand
   and the flat stick in your
   other hand.
4. Rub the flat stick across
   the top of the brush. Try to
   aim at the paper. Spray as
   much paint as you like on the paper.
   This is messy. but it is lots of fun. too.

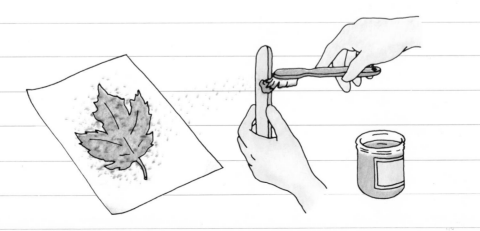

5. Then peel the leaf off the paper.

6. Let the leaf print sit until
   the paint is dry. It will
   look nifty when it is dry.

7. Leaf prints make pretty
   gifts for Mother's Day and for
   Father's Day.

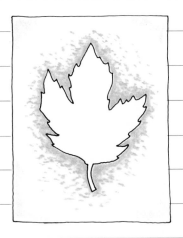

## Play Leap Frog
### by Sal, Tac, and Alf

1. First of all, get plenty of kids.
2. Have them stand in a line about four feet from each other.
3. Tell them to scrunch way down.
4. Go to the end of the line.
5. Jump like a frog over each person in the line.
6. When you get to the front of the line, you scrunch way down, too.
7. Tell the last person in line to jump over each kid.
8. Have that kid scrunch way down when he or she gets to the front of the line.
9. Keep playing, until each kid has jumped over all the other kids.

Teach leap frog to all your pals.
Just think how long the leap frog line will be then!

# Odd Socks
## by Oswald and Ettabetta

Things You Need:
a lot of socks
some little things that will fit
   in the socks
Try to get things that have
really odd shapes, like a jack,
a candle, a pine cone, a banana,
a hair pin, or a lump of clay.

1. First, put one odd thing in
   the bottom of each sock.
2. Then have your pals sit in
   a line.
3. Hand each of your pals a sock.
4. Tell them not to peek
   in the socks.
   That is a rule of the game!
5. Then let them feel the socks
   and try to name what is
   in them.
   We bet it is not very easy for
   them to tell!

## Make a Rain Suit for a Doll
### by Doc

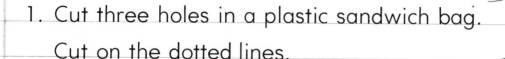

1. Cut three holes in a plastic sandwich bag. Cut on the dotted lines.
2. Put it on the doll.
3. Pin one of the scraps of plastic on the doll's hair for a rain hat. It will keep her hair from getting too frizzy.
4. Tape the other two plastic scraps on the doll's feet for galoshes. They will help her feet stay dry.

bottom of the bag

My plastic galoshes
Make splishes and sploshes
In mushes and slushes
Of mud!

# Make a Monster Mask
## by Tic and Cass

1. Get a paper shopping bag.
2. Cut holes in one side of the shopping bag.
3. Paint the mask with tempera paint. Blue and green paint are good to use.

4. Make long teeth out of white paper and tape them on the inside of the mask. The teeth will not really work. They will just look mean!

5. Make funny ears on the side of the mask. Cut flaps on the sides of the bag and bend them back.

Put on the mask and act like a monster!

13

# Feed a Bean Bag to a Dragon
## by Icky and Frits

1. Get a very big box..
2. Cut a hole in one side of the box.
3. Paint a hungry dragon on the same side of the box.
4. Get five bean bags.
5. Pick two teams. Have three kids on each team.
6. Make a line four feet from the dragon. The line will show the kids where to stand.

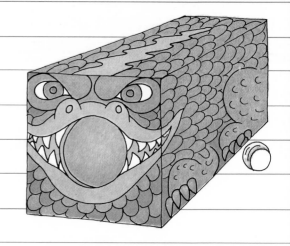

How to Play:
Dragons really like to eat
bean bags! The first kid on
one team will stand in
back of the line and toss five
bean bags to the dragon.

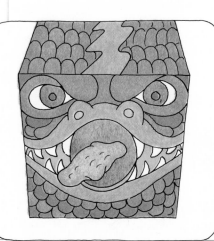

It is not easy to get the bean bags
in the hole. But don't go over
the line! Hungry dragons can be
very mean, if you get too close!
Keep track of how many bags each
kid feeds the dragon.

Next, a kid from the other team
will try to feed the dragon.
Keep going, until all the kids
have tried to feed the dragon.
The team that feeds the biggest
number of bean bags to the
dragon wins the game.

How many bean bags did your
dragon eat?

## Take a Nap
## by Toc

Lie down on a soft bed and sing
this song until you feel sleepy.

Dream of good things:
Like buttercup tea,
And a boat that floats across the sea,
And a spot in the shade of a peppermint tree,
And a ride on the wings of a bumblebee,
And feeling as happy as you can be.

Have sweet dreams.

# Chapter 2
## The Wish 18

| ier | iest |
|-----|------|
| easier | hungriest |
| happier | luckiest |
| sleepier | windiest |
| windier | |

their    now    always    because    been

fortune cookie    paper

# The Wish

Oswald was loaded down with beach
blankets and inner tubes. He tried
to run in the hot sand. His feet sank
down deep and sand filled his sneakers.

"Look at that lake!" he said. "I could
stay in there all day long."

"Last kid in the lake is a rotten fish!"
yelled Ettabetta.

The kids dived into the lake with
a splash! They kicked and screamed.
They rode on the waves and played
swimming games. At last Gus called,
"Time for lunch!"

"Let's go!" said Sal. "I am always
hungry. But now I am the hungriest
I have ever been! I think I could eat
a whale!"

The kids sat down to eat their lunches.
Lily reached into her beach bag for
a box of cookies. She passed a cookie
to each kid.

"What are these?" asked Doc.

"Fortune cookies," said Lily. "Your fortune
is in it. Crack it and see."

Doc broke the cookie. A white paper
fell out. The fortune said,

A person with freckles always brings you luck.

"That is me!" said Cass with a grin.

"This is fun," said Doc. "Hot Rod,
read your fortune now."

Hot Rod broke his cookie. His fortune
fell out. It said,

Run with the wind. Sing with the sun.
Always be glad.

"I like that," said Doc.

"Oswald, what is in your fortune cookie?"
asked Hot Rod.

Oswald looked at his fortune. It said.

This is your lucky day.
A wish you make may come true.

"Oh, you are the luckiest, Oswald!
Make a wish," said Ettabetta.

Oswald tried to think of a wish.
"I can't think of one now," he said.
"I think I will save it for a while."

"O.K.," said Ettabetta.

So Oswald saved his wish. The other
kids finished reading their fortunes.

After lunch, Oswald and Ettabetta
sat on the rocks. They looked at the boats.

"I have never been in a boat," said Oswald.
"I wish I could go sailing."

"<u>That</u> is a wish!" said Ettabetta.

"Yes, it is," said Oswald. "I <u>wish</u> I
could go sailing."

"But not now," said Ettabetta. "We don't
have a boat. Come on! Let's go for
another swim. Last one in the
lake is a rotten fish!"

Ettabetta jumped into the lake. But
Oswald did not want to swim. He felt sleepy.
He picked up an inner tube. He waded
into the waves. He lay on the tube and
began to float. He floated up and down,
up and down. The sun felt hot on his
chest. Oswald felt sleepier and sleepier.
Then he fell asleep.

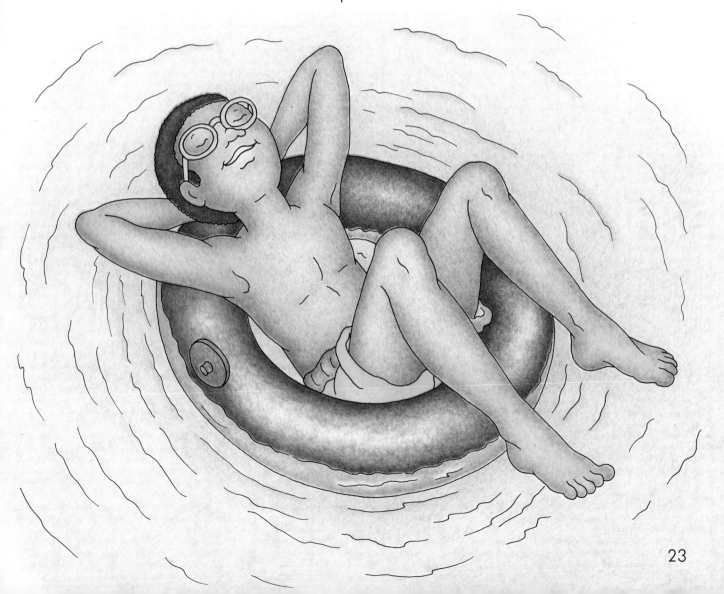

In a little while, the kids began to pack up their things. It was time to go.

"Where is Oswald?" asked Ettabetta.

"Isn't he with you?" asked Gus.

"No," said Ettabetta.

"Well, where is he?" asked Gert.

The kids began looking for Oswald. All of a sudden Ettabetta yelled, "Look! There he is! Out there!"

24

The kids looked. Oswald had drifted
way out into the middle of the lake.

The kids screamed and yelled and waved
their hands. But Oswald could not hear
them, because he was still sleeping.

"Screech! Screech!" screamed a gull.

It dived near the inner tube with a big splash.

PLOP!

Oswald woke up.

"Where am I?" he said.

Across the water he saw the kids waving.

"Oh, no!" he said. "I must have been
sleeping. I have drifted way out here.
How will I get back? My fortune said
this was my lucky day. But just look
at the mess I am in now!" He began
to feel afraid. "Help!" he yelled. "Help!"

Gert could hear Oswald yelling.
"He will be safe, because that tube
will keep him floating," she said.
"I will get a boat and pick him up."

"Wait!" said Ettabetta. "There is a boat.
It is sailing near Oswald. I think
it will pick him up."

"But it is so windy," said Lily. "It is
windier today than it has been any
other day. I hope the boat can get to
Oswald."

The boat sailed up to the inner tube.
A tall girl reached down and
grabbed Oswald.

"Here, get on the boat!" she yelled.

Oswald grabbed a rope and struggled on
to the boat. He was safe at last.

"Thanks a lot," he said to the girl.

"I am glad I could help you," she said.
"But I need a hand now. I could use
some help with these sails, because
this is the windiest day of the year.
It will be easier to sail the boat
if you help."

The girl handed Oswald a rope that was
attached to one of the sails.

Oswald leaned back and held the rope.
He felt the wind fill the sails.
He felt the waves go swish, swish
under the boat. He was much happier.
It was terrific to be sailing.
Oswald did not want the trip to end.

When the boat landed on the beach,
Oswald hopped out and thanked the girl.
Ettabetta ran up to him.

"Golly," she said. "Your wish came true.
This is the luckiest day you have ever had."

# Chapter 3
## The Super Day 33

baby

crazy

over

pony

shady

super

tiny

couldn't     wouldn't     weren't

We made this album after the trip to
Never Never Land. You can read it.
But please don't get fingerprints
on the snapshots!

Icky   Lily   Doc

Hot Rod   Oswald

Tac   Alf

Sal!

Frits   Toc

Tic

CASS

Ettabetta

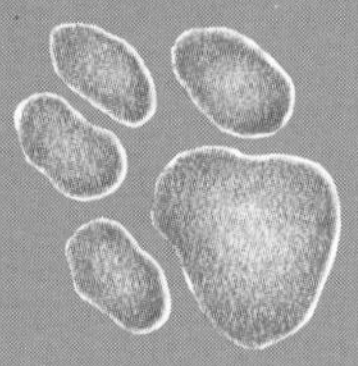

# The Super Day

One day Gus and Gert drove all
of us to Never Never Land.
Gert made this snapshot of us
when we got there. We couldn't
wait to go on all the rides.

It was Kids' Day at Never Never Land.
All kids could get in free! We didn't
need tickets to go on the rides.
They just stamped each kid's hand.
This is Icky's hand.

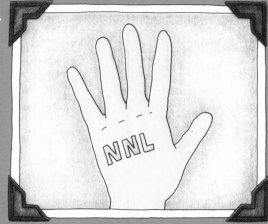

Frits and Doc went on a ride
called Over the Falls. They got in
a boat and went into a tunnel.
Up, up, up they went. They reached
the top of a steep hill. Zip!
Down they came. SPLASH! Over the falls!
They got all wet. They had to sit in a
sunny spot to dry. But they weren't upset.

Sal pitched five balls at some empty bottles. He hit them all. When the last bottle fell over, the man gave him a prize! It was a fluffy, shocking-pink monster doll. Sal said it was the neatest thing he had ever gotten.

Then Lily, Icky, and Toc tried to tip over the bottles. But they couldn't hit very many. They didn't get fluffy, shocking-pink monster dolls. They just got these junky little hats.

This is us in the Monster Tunnel.
We couldn't see very well because it was dark.
But that was O.K. with us.
We were all afraid.

Some of the kids liked the
Animal Shed at Never Never Land
the best. We could look at lots
of animals. There were baby goats, sheep,
rabbits, ducks, a mule, and a pony.
The animal we liked best was this
itty-bitty tiny piggy. We named
it Taffy. Isn't it the sweetest
little thing?

Hot Rod and Ettabetta went on
the Ferris wheel. They got stuck
on the top for the longest time
while the people on the bottom
got off. Hot Rod couldn't look down.
Ettabetta held on to the seat.
It is not fun to be stuck up there.
We all cheered when they got down.

We stopped for a while to eat lunch. We got some hot dogs from a hot dog stand. The hot dogs were very good. They were yummy in the tummy!

We sat on the grass under a big, shady oak tree. It was fun just to look at the people passing by.

This was the oddest thing we saw
all day. It was a trash can and
it spoke to us! It said, "My name
is Cubby. I like to eat trash.
Feed your trash to me."
Alf put some trash up to Cubby's lips.
Swish! Cubby sucked the trash
out of Alf's hand.

Golly liked that trick!

Cass got a fluffy ball of
cotton candy. It was
very sticky. She gave
each of us a bite.
It was very sweet.

After lunch, we made Gus and Gert
go on the Lucky Ducky. They
wouldn't go on any of the other rides,
but they went on the Lucky Ducky.
They looked very silly sitting
with all those little kids.
We couldn't stop giggling at them!
Weren't they funny!

Tac and Oswald went on the
Twist Up. It kept spinning
and spinning. It really twisted
them up. When they got off
the ride, they were so dizzy
they couldn't stand up. They just
kept giggling and falling down.
They acted crazy.

The fastest ride in Never Never Land was The Streak. We wouldn't leave Never Never Land until we had a ride on it! We waited and waited in line to go on The Streak. At last we got on. We were off, lickety-split! We went up and down the hills as fast as the wind. We screamed all the way. We held on to the seats. We held on to each other. At last we came to a stop. We had so much fun we went on The Streak another time.

At last it was time to go home.
Gert made this snapshot of us
on the way back. You can see that
all the Superkids had a super day
at Never Never Land!

# Chapter 4

## Fire! 44
## It Is Hot 56
## The Super Hiding Spot 59

| <u>ar</u> | <u>er</u> | <u>ir</u> | <u>or</u> | <u>ur</u> |
|-----------|-----------|-----------|-----------|-----------|
| alarm | another | dirt | corner | burn |
| apartment | brother | girl | for | burned |
| Carmen | covered | third | morning | burning |
| department | disaster | | porch | curled |
| farther | discover | | reporter | fur |
| hardly | everyone | | Salvador | hurry |
| marching | father | | sort | hurt |
| part | mother | | storms | returning |
| started | other | | story | Thursday |
| Vargas | scattered | | | turned |

cold    know    does    laugh    both    again

fire chief    fire fighters

# Fire!

RING! RING!

Chief Flinn picked up the .
"Fire Department Number Six," he said.
"This is Chief Flinn. What? I can't
understand you. I don't speak Spanish.
Wait!"

The chief turned to the fire fighters.
"Does anybody know how to speak Spanish?"
yelled the fire chief.

"I know Spanish," said Sal.

"Good," said the chief. "Quick!
Come and speak to this girl."

"She said there is a fire!" said Sal.

"Get the address!" said the chief.

Sal spoke to the girl again.
"The fire is on White Street!" he said.

45

The fire chief rang the alarm and the
fire fighters came running. They put on their
hats and coats as they jumped on the
fire truck. The truck was all set to go.

VRUM! VRUM! VRUM!

People in the streets scattered as
the truck rushed by.

The fire chief called to Sal.
"Come with us," he said. "We can both
ride in my car. I will need your help."

Sal jumped into the red car with
the chief and they sped off.

All the traffic stopped as the fire truck streaked by. As it turned the corner onto White Street, Sal could see big puffs of gray smoke. The red car screeched to a stop.

"Let's go!" said the fire chief. A little girl ran up to the chief and grabbed his arm.

"My mother! My father! My sisters and brothers!" yelled the little girl in Spanish. "They are trapped!"

"Quick!" yelled Sal to the chief. "Her family is trapped upstairs! There they are!"

The smoke from the burning fire was turning the sky black.

"Hurry. Get the ladder up!" yelled the chief.

¡Mi mamá! ¡Mi papá! ¡Mis hermanos! ¡Están arriba!

The big ladder went up, up, up to the top
of the apartment. The fire fighters rushed up the ladder.

Everything happened very quickly.
Some of the fire fighters helped get
the family down the ladder. Other fire fighters
sprayed the flames with the hose.

At last the fire was out. The back porch
and part of the kitchen were burned,
but the family was safe. The mother
and father thanked the fire chief
again and again.

Just then a car drove up. A reporter
for the <u>Morning</u> <u>Star</u> got out.

"Is the fire out?" asked the reporter.

"Yes!" said the chief. "And everyone
is safe."

"Good!" said the reporter. "It looks like
you and your fire fighters saved the day."

"We had a lot of help," said Chief Flinn. "Without these two kids, the fire would have been a real disaster. Carmen called the Fire Department quickly. Sal knows how to speak Spanish. He spoke to her about the fire. Both Sal and Carmen are the real stars of this adventure."

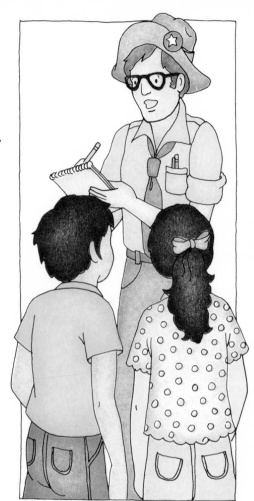

"That is terrific," said the reporter. "Tell me about it."

Sal and Carmen both spoke to the reporter. Sal explained what Carmen said in Spanish. When the reporter left, Sal and the fire chief went back to the Fire Department. Carmen and her family began cleaning up their home.

The next day, the front page of the Morning Star looked like this:

# MORNING

## FAMILY IS SAVED FROM BURNING HOME

### Two Kids Help Fire Department

A fire broke out yesterday morning in the home of the J. W. Vargas family at 19 White Street. Carmen Vargas discovered the fire. The rest of the family was trapped upstairs.

Thursday, June 18

Carmen quickly called the Fire Department. Luckily, Salvador Mirandez was visiting the Fire Department when Carmen's call came in. Carmen speaks only Spanish. Salvador explained what Carmen was saying to the fire chief.

Fire Chief Flinn said, "Without the help of both those children, that fire would have been a disaster!"

# It Is Hot

Gosh! It is hot!
Can't you see the street shimmer?
Don't you feel your skin simmer?
Does the pavement burn your feet?
Want to play?

I do not.
It is too hot.

Gosh! It is hot!
But we could sit in the shade
And pretend a parade
Is marching down the street.
Want to play?

I do not.
It is too hot.

Gosh! It is hot.
The sun seems to be humming.
No, a fire truck is coming.
Let's chase it down the street.
Want to play?

I do not.
It is too hot.

57

It is so hot.

The fire chief opened a pipe, see!

Now look! He is calling you and me!

There are rivers in the street!

Want to play?

I do!
Don't you?

# The Super Hiding Spot

The Superkids were playing Hide
and Seek. Tic was It. She began calling,
"One, two, three, four, five . . ."
The kids all scattered to hide.
Toc hid under a big box. Alf hid in back
of a bench. Frits hid in an empty trash can.
Icky hid inside a big pipe.

"O.K. Here I come!" hollered Tic.

Icky began to laugh softly. He could see Tic looking all over. He could hear her yell, "I see Frits, one-two-three, hiding in the trash can!" He could hear her yell, "I see Tac, one-two-three, hiding in back of the car!"

"Their hiding spots are not as good as mine," laughed Icky. "Tic will never discover me."

Icky waited and waited. Tic came close
to the pipe, but she didn't peek inside.
After a little while, she went away.
Icky smiled. He was safe in the pipe.

"She does not know where I am," he said
to himself. "I will wait a little longer.
Then I will run in free."

PING. PING. PING.

"What is that?" Icky asked.

PING. PING. PING.

Rain was falling on the pipe. It fell
quickly, in big drops.

"Oh, no," said Icky. "Now I am stuck.
If I try to run in free, I know I will
get soaked. I will have to wait until
the rain stops."

Icky could hear the Superkids running
to get out of the rain. They went
farther and farther away. At last,
Icky could not hear them at all.
All he could hear was the rain
gushing from the angry, dark sky.
Icky saw a flash streak out of the sky.
He put his hands over his ears and
waited for the crash of thunder.

CRASH! CRACK! RUMBLE, RUMBLE, MUMBLE.

It felt like the thunder was inside
the pipe.

Another flash zig-zagged across the sky.
Icky scrunched his legs up to his chest.
He began to shiver. He covered his ears.
He was cold and scared.

Suddenly a wet ball of fur shot into
the pipe. It snuggled up to Icky.

"Golly! You wet mutt! What are you
doing here?" asked Icky.

Golly stared up at Icky with a sad look.
He tried to put all four of his paws in
Icky's lap. He squeezed in so close that Icky
could hardly sit up.

"Golly, you are soaking wet and you are cold. Are you sick?" asked Icky.

Thunder rumbled outside the pipe again and Golly shivered harder. Then Icky began to understand.

"I know," he said. "You are not just cold. You are scared. Does the storm scare you? Well, thunderstorms won't hurt you. In fact, some thunderstorms are sort of fun to see. Look at me. I am not afraid."

Icky tried to look brave. Golly wagged his tail a little bit. Icky patted Golly's back. He scratched in back of Golly's ears.

Icky looked down at Golly. He wasn't shaking any more. Icky smiled. Both he and Golly were wet, but Icky didn't care. They both felt safe. They weren't scared any more. It was much easier to be brave when someone needed your help.

The rain kept falling. Icky saw it make
puddles in the dirt. Golly curled up
and went to sleep.

At last, the thunder stopped rumbling
and the rain stopped falling. Icky could
hear the kids returning. Quickly,
he dashed out of the pipe. Golly ran
after him.

"One, two, three, all in free!" yelled Icky.
And he started to laugh.

"Icky!" said Tic. "I looked everywhere
for you. Were you hiding all this time?
Didn't the storm scare you? Where were you?"

Icky smiled at Tic. "I had the best
hiding spot of all," he said with a laugh.
"Only Golly knows where it was. And Golly
will never, ever tell."

# Chapter 5

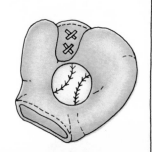

<u>oi</u>                    <u>oy</u>

coins                   annoy

disappointed            boy

join                    enjoy

moist

pointed

soil

spoil

spoiled

spoils

kind    buy    find    right    wash    light

grow

# For the Birds

JOIN PROJECT GREEN

Plant a garden.
Free garden plots in back
of Government Hall.
Just bring the seeds. We will put
your name on the list
for a garden.
Come to Government Hall!

"Boy, it would be lots
of fun to plant a garden
this summer," said Alf.

"Let's go ask the kids if
they want to do it," said Toc.

Alf and Toc ran to the bus.

"Who wants to join Project Green and plant a garden this summer?" asked Toc.

"I do! I do!" said all the kids.

"Terrific! Now all we have to do is buy some seeds," said Alf.

"Buy seeds?" said Hot Rod. "I don't have any cash."

"We can use the cash we have saved up
in the club bank," said Doc. She got
the club bank and dumped the coins in
her lap. "Oh, good! We have lots of cash.
We can buy a lot of seeds," she said.

"Toc and I will go to Government Hall,"
said Alf. "We will put our names on the
list for a garden plot. You kids go
buy the seeds."

The kids split up. Alf and Toc ran all the way to Government Hall. When they got there, there was a long line of people waiting to get garden plots.

"It looks like we got here just in time," said Alf. Alf and Toc went to the end of the line and began to wait.

"A garden will be so much fun," said Toc. "Just think, we can plant fresh corn and beans."

"Right! And some big red beets," said Alf. "Yum!"

Toc and Alf had to wait and wait.
"My feet hurt," said Alf.

"What a long line," said Toc.

At last Alf and Toc got to the front
of the line. The person at Government
Hall handed them a map of all the garden
plots. She put a star on a plot for
the Superkids' garden. It was plot
number four.

"This is the best plot I can find,"
she said with a smile. "It gets plenty
of light. It is just right for you kids."

"Oh, thank you!" said Alf and Toc.

They rushed back to the bus
with the map. "Look! Look!" they yelled.
"We got a plot! We can find our plot
with this map. Did you get seeds?
What kind did you get?"

Hot Rod said, "We got all kinds!
Tac and I got corn seeds. Oswald and
Lily got carrot seeds. Ettabetta and
Sal are going to plant beans."

"Peas for Tic and me," said Doc.

"Radishes for me!" yelled Frits.

"And beets for Icky and me!" said Cass.

"That is terrific!" said Alf. "What kind
of seeds did you get for us?"

"For you?" said Hot Rod.

The kids all looked at each other.
"We forgot to get seeds for you, and
we spent all the cash," said Doc.

Alf and Toc looked disappointed.

"But that is not right!" said Toc.
"Alf and I waited in line all morning
to get a plot. And you didn't even buy
one seed for us?"

"We are sorry. We just forgot," said Doc.

"That is rotten," said Alf.

"Well, why don't you all get started
without us?" said Toc.

So the other kids left.

"Boy, this really spoils the garden for me," said Alf. "I don't have a penny to buy seeds."

"There must be something we could plant that does not cost anything," said Toc. "Maybe we can find some seeds. Do you have any at home?"

"Well, we do have some kind of bird seed!" said Alf.

"Maybe we could plant bird seed," said Toc. "I bet it would grow."

"Well, let's try it," said Alf.

Toc and Alf ran to the backyard.

"There is the bird feeder," said Alf.
He pointed to the branch of a tree.
"I will lift you up and you can grab
a handful of seeds. I don't
think the birds will miss it."

"O.K.," said Toc. "But be careful."

Alf lifted Toc up to the bird feeder.
She grabbed a handful of seeds and
put them in her pocket.

"Let's go to the garden. I can't
wait to plant these!" Toc said.

The other kids had dug up the garden plot. First they had to pull out lots of weeds. Then they began to plant the seeds in the soil.

Toc pointed to a spot in the back of the garden. "Let's plant our seeds over there," she said. "There will be lots of light right there."

"O.K." said Alf. Alf and Toc began to pull out weeds from their part of the garden.

"What are you going to plant?" asked Hot Rod.

"Bird seed!" said Toc with a smile. She held out her hand with the seeds in it.

The kids began to laugh. "Are you going to grow birds?" giggled Tic.

"Tweet, tweet, tweet!" laughed Tac.

"Come on, Toc," said Alf. "Don't let them spoil our fun."

Alf and Toc planted the bird seed.
They covered the seeds with soil and
then sprinkled them with a hose. Each day
Toc and Alf checked to see if the soil was
moist. Each day they checked to see
if the seeds had started to grow.
And each day the kids made fun of Alf
and Toc.

"How is your tweet weed growing?"
laughed Cass and Hot Rod.

"Do you have any bird blossoms yet?"
giggled Icky.

"Those kids are beginning to annoy me!"
said Toc.

"Yes, me too," said Alf. "What fun
is a garden if you can't enjoy it?"

After a while, all the Superkids' seeds
began to grow. The garden was full of
little green plants popping out of the soil.
The carrots began to pop up.
The radishes began to pop up.
The corn and beans began to pop up.
The beets began to pop up.
And to everyone's surprise, something
began to pop up from the bird seed!

Each day the bird seed plants got bigger and bigger and taller and taller. They were much taller than Oswald and Lily's carrots. They were much taller than Ettabetta and Sal's beans or Doc and Tic's peas. They were even taller than Tac and Hot Rod's corn.

"Boy, my radishes look sick next to those bird seed plants," said Frits.

All summer long, the bird seed plants got bigger and better. The kids stopped making fun of Alf and Toc. And then, one day, a fantastic thing happened. The bird seed plants blossomed!

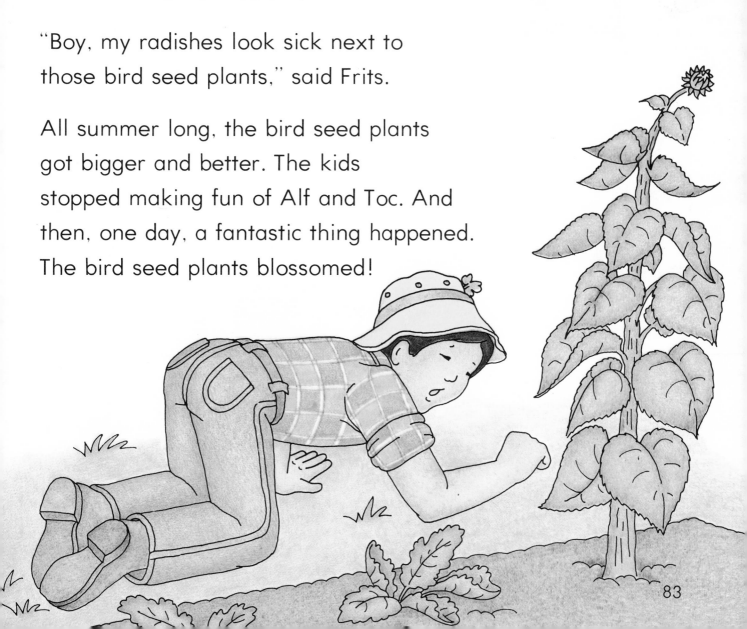

"Is that bird seed plant pretty!" said Doc. "It looks like the sun with a dark tummy!"

"I have never seen a plant like that," said Hot Rod. "It is so tall!"

"That is the best plant in the garden," said Tac.

"Thank you," said Alf and Toc.

Just then a bird landed on the blossom and began to chirp and sing. Toc began to laugh. "You see, we did grow birds after all!"

# The Lost Mitt

"Gosh, Frits, what a neat baseball
mitt," Ettabetta said.

"Yes, this is a pretty good mitt,"
Frits said, as he punched it with his fist.

Ettabetta looked at Frits. She said
sadly, "I have been saving for months to buy
that kind of mitt. But I still need more cash.
And I could really use a mitt today.
My team has a big game after lunch."

"I will lend you my mitt," said Frits.
"I don't need it today."

"You will?" said Ettabetta. "Oh, boy!
Thanks, Frits. That is terrific!
I will return it in the morning."

Frits tossed the mitt to Ettabetta
and she grabbed it with one hand.

"Good catch!" said Frits with a laugh.

Ettabetta waved, and off she ran.

After lunch, the kids played their ball game.
In the last seconds of the game,
Ettabetta's team was winning.
Ettabetta punched Frits's mitt and
whispered, "Come on, mitt, we can do it.
Only one more catch and we win
the game."

WHAM! The batter hit the ball. The ball
went way up into the sky.

"Catch it! Catch it!" yelled the kids on her team.

Ettabetta ran to the left, then back,
then to the left some more. Then she
stretched way back and held the mitt up
in the air.

THUD!

The ball landed right in the middle of the mitt.
All the kids began to clap and cheer happily.

Ettabetta was so happy, she tossed
the mitt up in the air and began to jump
up and down. All the kids rushed up
to her and said, "What a fantastic catch!"
It had been the best game Ettabetta
had ever played.

When Ettabetta went to bed that evening,
she could hardly get to sleep. She kept
seeing that last ball fly into the air.
She remembered running to catch it.
Then, THUD! It landed in Frits's wonderful
mitt and all the fans cheered. She could
never have won the game without
Frits's mitt.

Suddenly, she sat right up in bed.
"Frits's mitt!" she said to herself. "Oh, no!
Where is it?" She felt horrible.
"Where have I left it?" she asked herself.
"I must have left it at the ball park.
But what will I do if I can't find it?
Oh, this is awful."

Now everything was spoiled. Ettabetta
was so upset that she hardly slept at all.

As soon as the sun came up and it was
light out, Ettabetta went right to the
ball park to look for the mitt.
"It has to be here somewhere," she said.
She looked under the bench.
She looked everywhere. But there was
no mitt.

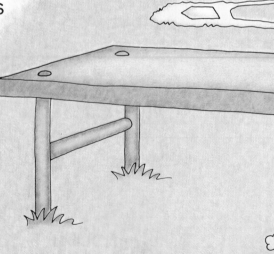

"Oh, no," said Ettabetta sadly. "Frits will be so mad if I have lost his mitt. What can I do? I just can't tell him!" Ettabetta went back to the bench and sat down. She had to think.

Then she remembered her savings. "Maybe I can make that extra cash this morning. I can buy Frits the same kind of mitt! Maybe he won't even know that it is different. Then I won't have to tell him I lost his mitt. And then he won't get mad at me!"

Ettabetta went to see if Gus and Gert
had any jobs. They did. First she had
to wash and wax a car. Then she put out
the trash. Then she washed two more cars.
By the end of the morning, she had made
the extra cash she needed.

Ettabetta grabbed her piggy bank and
ran to the Sports Shop. She paid for
the new mitt.

After lunch, Ettabetta went looking for Frits. He was reading comics at the bus. Ettabetta tossed the new mitt to him. She hoped he would not know it was a different one. She smiled and said, "Frits, your mitt was super. It helped us win the game. Thanks a lot."

Frits looked surprised. He said, "This is a pretty good mitt, Ettabetta. But it is not mine."

Ettabetta gulped. "It is your mitt now," she said sadly. "I can't find the other one, Frits. I was afraid to tell you, so I washed some cars and made some cash to buy a new mitt."

"But, Ettabetta," Frits said, "I have
my mitt. Icky picked it up after the game.
He gave it to me this morning. It has
my name and address printed right inside it."

"Really?" said Ettabetta.

"Really," said Frits. He tossed the new
mitt to Ettabetta. "But now you have
the mitt you wanted. Let's play catch!"

# Chapter 6

| <u>ar</u> | <u>ear</u> | <u>or</u> |
|-----------|------------|-----------|
| dollars | earth | doctor |
| forward | heard | word |
| | learn | work |
| | | working |

I'll    you'll    she'll    they'll    he'll    we'll

eyes    Mrs.

# Slumber Party

Tic, Lily, and Cass set up a tent in Tic's backyard. "We'll have a real slumber party," said Tic happily.

"Boy, it is going to be fun to sleep outside," said Cass.

"Yes, sleeping in a tent is neat," said Tic. But Lily did not say a word. This was the first time she had ever slept away from home, and she was a little bit afraid.

When the tent was set up, the girls put on their pajamas. They snuggled into their sleeping bags and began to whisper and giggle. It was very dark inside the tent.

"I'll tell a scary story," said Tic.

"Oh, no!" said Lily.

"Oh, yes!" said Cass.

"I have a good story," said Tic. "You'll like it." And she began to tell it very softly.

One day a little boy was going down the road when he saw a pot. It was full of silver dollars. He stopped to pick up the pot. "Gosh!" said the little boy. "Wait until my mother sees this! She'll be so happy." He put the pot under his arm and ran home.

But the boy did not know that the pot of silver dollars belonged to an ugly goblin! And a goblin would never let go of a pot of silver. Later, when the little boy went to sleep, the ugly goblin came to visit him.

"Whooo stole my pot of silver dollars?" said the goblin. "Whooo stole my pot of silver dollars?"

The little boy woke up. "I must be dreaming!" he said to himself. But the ugly goblin came closer and closer.

"Whooo stole my pot of silver dollars?" he asked. The little boy felt something tapping his leg. "Whooo stole my pot of silver dollars? Was it YOU?"

And just as she said "YOU,"
Tic jumped up and grabbed Lily.

"Eek!" screamed Lily.

"Yikes!" screamed Cass.

Tic began to laugh. Then Cass began
to laugh. But Lily did not laugh.

"Boy, that was a good story," said Cass.
"Where did you learn it?"

"I heard it from my sister," said Tic.

"I liked it," said Cass. But Lily didn't
say a word.

"It is nine o'clock," said Cass. "It is
time to go to sleep." The girls snuggled
deeper into their sleeping bags. It was
very still. And it was very, very dark.

Lily tried to go to sleep, but she just couldn't.
Just thinking about the dark made her
afraid. Most of the time she was brave.
She tried very hard to be brave now,
but it was so dark. And she kept thinking
about the scary story.

"Maybe goblins are real," Lily said
to herself. "Oh, why did Tic tell that
scary story?" All of a sudden, Lily
felt something wiggle near the bottom
of her sleeping bag. Now she was
really scared.

"What if that is a goblin? Maybe he'll
get us!" said Lily softly to herself.
She lay very still and waited. "I bet
it is a goblin. And I bet he'll get us!"
Again she felt the wiggle at the bottom
of her sleeping bag.

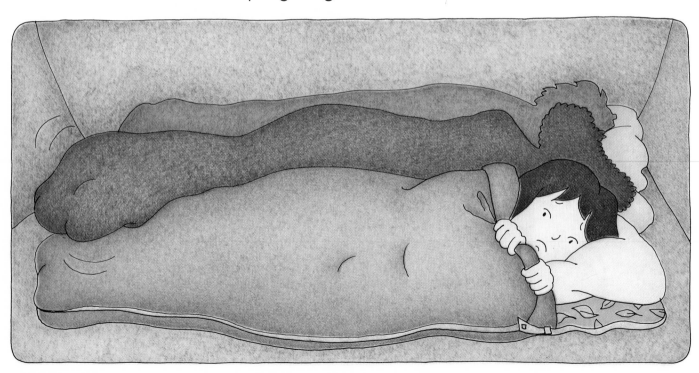

There was something down there.
It wiggled again. Lily screamed and sat up.
She grabbed the end of her sleeping bag.

"Go away, go away!" she yelled.

"What is the matter with you?" said Tic.
"Let go of my feet!"

"Oh, no," said Lily. "Are those your feet?"
Suddenly she could not keep back the tears.

"Oh, Lily, what is the matter?" asked Cass.

"I am afraid of the dark," said Lily.

"Gosh," said Cass. "Why didn't you say so?"

"I used to be afraid of the dark, too,"
said Tic. "But I'll show you a wonderful
thing." She lifted the tent flaps.
"Look up there," she said, and she pointed
to the sky.

Cass and Lily looked out. It was light
outside the tent. The sky was full of stars.

"You see, when it is dark, the stars
shine in the sky. You won't be
afraid, if you'll remember the stars are
shining for you," said Tic. "They'll light up
the sky and they'll cheer you up."

"The stars are pretty," said Lily.
She looked up at them. She saw one big star
shining over the tent. It winked at her.
Lily blinked. The star winked again. Lily smiled.

"Do you think you can go to sleep now?"
asked Tic.

"Yes, I think so," said Lily. "I'll try."
She lay back. She felt much better as
she looked up at the sky. In a little
while she was fast asleep.
Over the tent,
the stars glittered
and sparkled
and twinkled
and winked.

# Star Gazing

If you live where the stars are hard
to see, you can make stars.

To make stars, you'll need a carton,
a tack, and a flashlight.

First, you'll need to poke holes in the
bottom of the carton with the tack.

Next, turn on the flashlight and turn
off all the lamps.

Put the flashlight in the carton and
shine your stars up on the wall.

Turn your flashlight on and off
to make the stars wink and blink.

# The Runaway Dragon

Hot Rod and Doc were standing near the bus.

"Gosh," said Doc. "I haven't seen Oswald
for a week.

"I'll bet he is working on a big project,"
said Hot Rod. "Maybe he'll surprise us with it."

Suddenly, Oswald came running out of
the bus. He had a little box with four
buttons on it.

"It is finished!" he yelled. "Oh, boy! Wait till you see this!"

He pushed a purple button. Something in the bus began to whiz and whir.

"Stand back! Both of you!" he said.

Just then, something came flying out of the bus. It had big flashing eyes and a horrible red grin.

"Yikes!" yelled Hot Rod.

"A dragon!" gasped Doc.

"Watch out!" called Oswald.

The dragon dipped and dived over the
kids. Oswald pushed each button.
The dragon went up. The dragon went down.
The dragon wiggled from side to side.
Oswald could make the dragon do
whatever he wanted it to do.
At last he turned a red button.
The dragon landed safely at his feet.

"Gosh!" said Doc. "That is terrific!
How does it work?"

"Simple," said Oswald. "I'll show you."

He picked up the dragon and held it in
both hands. "There is a model plane
inside the dragon. That is what makes it
fly. This black box makes the plane work."

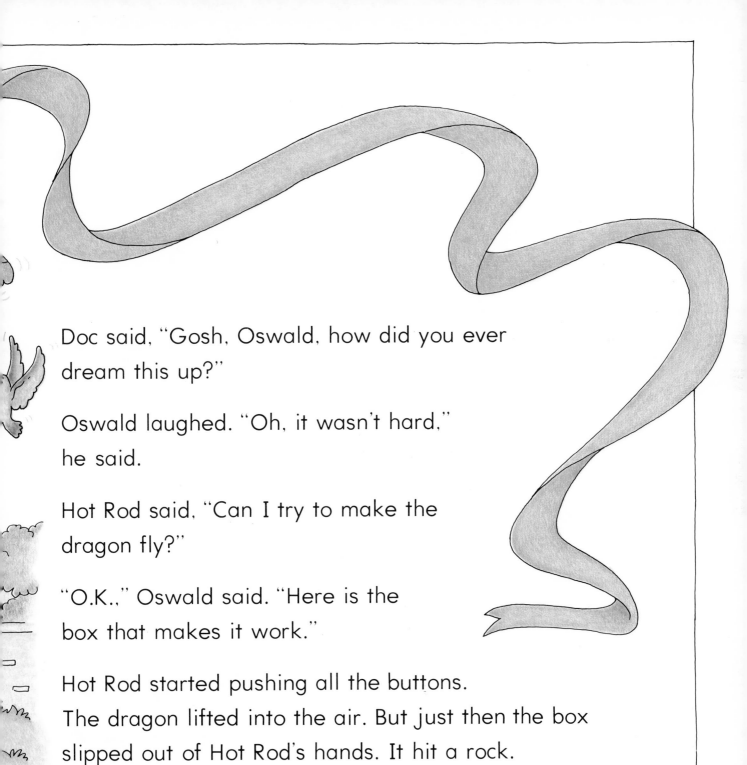

Doc said, "Gosh, Oswald, how did you ever dream this up?"

Oswald laughed. "Oh, it wasn't hard," he said.

Hot Rod said, "Can I try to make the dragon fly?"

"O.K.," Oswald said. "Here is the box that makes it work."

Hot Rod started pushing all the buttons. The dragon lifted into the air. But just then the box slipped out of Hot Rod's hands. It hit a rock.

"Oh, no!" he said. "I hope I didn't spoil it!" And he started to pick up the black box.

"Look out!" yelled Doc. "Get down or we'll get hit."

Hot Rod and Oswald ducked!

The dragon made a dive at them. Then it twirled and whirled and went flying over the trees.

Oswald picked up the black box. He pushed each button. Nothing happened. The dragon kept on going.

"It doesn't work! We broke the buttons!" cried Oswald. "I can't bring the dragon back! Quick! We'll have to catch it, or the dragon will crash!"

The kids started to run, but they couldn't catch up to the dragon.

It was flying very fast. Its big eyes sparkled like shining suns. Its long green tail flapped in the breeze. Up, up, up it went. Quickly it was over the trees. Then it turned a corner and they could not see it at all.

In a little while, the dragon came flying over Main Street. It dipped and dived over the stores.

A bird!

A dragon!

Everyone ran out into the street. Mrs. Dearing was rubbing her eyes and looking up at the sky.

"What happened?" asked Gus.

"I don't know," said Mrs. Dearing. "This big thing dived out of the sky at me. It had flashing eyes and a horrible red grin. It looked like a DRAGON! I must be seeing things! I need to see a doctor."

Oswald, Doc, and Hot Rod came running down the street. They saw the people standing in front of the stores. The three kids yelled, "Has anyone seen a dragon?"

Everyone started jabbering.

What on earth was that?

Just then, Ben came running up
the street. He stopped in front of
the people and said, "Has anyone seen
Polly, my parrot? Something green
came flying past my shop. Polly
saw it. She cried, 'Pretty Bird.'
Then she hopped off her perch and went
flying after it. Now she is lost."

"Oh, no," groaned Oswald. "This is awful."

Everyone looked at Oswald. "Polly is chasing my paper dragon," he said.

Ben just laughed. He said, "Silly Polly. Wait till she finds out that her 'Pretty Bird' is a paper dragon. She'll be so disappointed."

"Look!" said a little boy. He pointed up in the air. "There they are!"

Everyone looked up.

"My dragon!" said Oswald.

"My parrot!" said Ben. "Come back here, Polly," he cried. "Come back!"

"Pretty Bird!" squawked the parrot. "Pretty Bird!"

Up in the sky, the dragon and Polly
dipped and twirled and dived and whirled.
Down on the street, Oswald and Ben ran to
the left, then forward, then back, then
to the left again. Oswald was getting dizzy.

Suddenly, the dragon started to fall.

"Oh, no!" Oswald cried. "My dragon is
going to crash!"

But Polly grabbed the dragon in her claws. She held on to it. Then she flapped her wings very hard. The dragon and the parrot landed with a soft thud.

Oswald ran over to his dragon. He could see that it was hurt. It would take a long time to fix it.

"Oh, my silly runaway dragon," said Oswald.

"Oh, my silly runaway Polly!" laughed Ben.

"Oh, my!" squawked Polly. "Oh, my! Pretty Bird!"

# Chapter 7
## The Lesson 122
## That Was Yesterday 133

| ow | ou | ow |
|----|----|----|
| crowd | about | follow |
| crowded | around | show |
| downtown | counted | window |
| flowers | crouched | |
| frowned | found | |
| frowning | grouch | |
| how | ground | |
| howled | ouch | |
| now | out | |
| Powers | shouted | |
| scowled | | |
| wow | | |

warm    walk    give    once    done

house    Ms.

# The Lesson

"Hot Rod has only been to the bus once this week," said Cass. "I wonder what he is doing these days."

Oswald said, "I just saw him. I asked him where he was going. But he wouldn't tell me. He was pretty grumpy about it, too."

"That is odd," said Cass. "Maybe he needs help. Let's go find him."

"O.K.," said Oswald. "Hot Rod was starting to ride downtown when I saw him. Let's follow him."

Cass and Oswald rode off on their bikes. When they got to Second Street, Cass spotted Hot Rod's bike. It was parked in front of an apartment house. Cass said, "Hot Rod must be inside. But what do you suppose he is doing in there?"

"Let's go see," said Oswald. Cass and Oswald left their bikes and walked over to the apartment house. They heard a tune coming from a window. They crouched down next to the window.

"I hear someone playing an instrument," said Cass. The tune came from inside.

Bee bop ditty ditty wow wow,
Bee bop ditty ditty wonk wonk!

The tune stopped. Then a woman inside said, "You made a mistake, Hot Rod. Would you play that tune once again?"

Bee bop ditty ditty wow wow,
Bee bop ditty ditty wonk wonk!

"Oh, no," said Hot Rod. "I give up. Ms. Powers, I will never play that tune the right way. The clarinet is too hard. It is no fun anymore. I want to quit my clarinet lessons."

Ms. Powers said, "Oh, don't give up!
That would be a big mistake, Hot Rod.
It takes a long time to get very good.
I think you have done quite well.
I want you to play your clarinet
in the Talent Show on Saturday."

"But I don't want to play anymore,"
said Hot Rod.

"Oh, Hot Rod," said Ms. Powers, "give
it a try. Then, if you still want to quit
after the Talent Show, I will
understand."

"Well, O.K.," said Hot Rod. "But I
really hope the Superkids don't come
to the show. I don't want them to
make fun of me."

"Let's get out of here," whispered Cass.
"Hot Rod would be mad if he found us."

Cass and Oswald went back to the bus.
Cass said, "I think it is terrific that
Hot Rod can play the clarinet. I am going
to the Talent Show. I want to hear
him play."

"I do, too," said Oswald. "Let's get
all the kids to go. We can meet at my
house and walk to the show together.
But let's not tell the kids that Hot Rod is
in the show! It will be a surprise
for them."

Saturday came at last. All the Superkids met to walk to the show. When they got to the hall, they all sat together.

First a little girl played the drums. BOOM! BOOM! BLAM! BLAM! Then a tall boy sang a song about flowers.

Sal yawned. "What is so good about this?" he asked.

Ettabetta began to wiggle in her seat. "Why did you make us come to this talent show?" she said to Cass.

"Just wait and you'll see," said Cass.

Then two girls played trumpets.
Doc and Cass clapped. They liked the
trumpets. Then a boy played the harmonica.

The hall was getting warm. Alf began
to squirm. "This is so boring,"
he whispered to Sal. "And it is
so warm in here. I wish I were
home. I like TV better than this."

"Just you wait," said Cass.

Just then, someone began to play a
jazzy tune.

Bee bop ditty ditty wow wow,
Bee bop ditty ditty wow wow wow!

"Oh, wow!" said Icky. "It is Hot Rod!
I didn't know he could play the clarinet!"

"He is really good!" said Doc.

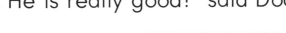

129

Hot Rod played another tune. The crowd
snapped their fingers and tapped their
feet. When Hot Rod was done,
everyone clapped.

After the show, Ms. Powers went up
to Hot Rod. She said, "You have done
very well. Thank you for being in the show.
How do you feel about the clarinet now?"

"Well," said Hot Rod. "It is not so bad.
But I still want to give up my lessons."

Just then, the Superkids came running up to Hot Rod. They all began to speak at once.

Hot Rod, you are terrific!

How do you do it?

Is it hard?

We didn't know you could play the clarinet!

Show us how.

Hot Rod began to play.

Bee bop ditty ditty wow wow,
Bee bop ditty ditty wow wow wow!

"That is the best thing I ever heard!"
said Cass. "Can you give me clarinet
lessons, Hot Rod?"

"That would be fun," said Hot Rod.
"But first I have to take more lessons
myself! It takes a long time to get
very good."

Bee bop ditty ditty wow wow,
Bee bop ditty ditty wow wee!

# That Was Yesterday

One warm day the Superkids were at the park. They were playing a game of tag.

"I am it!" shouted Frits. Frits counted to ten. "1, 2, 3, 4, 5, 6, 7, 8, 9, 10! Look out! Here I come!"

Alf ran past Frits. "You can't catch me! You can't catch me!" chanted Alf.

Frits began to chase Alf. When he got close to Alf, Frits reached out his hand as far as it would go. "I got you! You are it!" shouted Frits.

"I am not!" shouted Alf. "You missed me by a mile."

"I did not! I tagged you!" yelled Frits.

"You never came close," hollered Alf.

"Want to make a bet?" asked Frits.

"O.K.!" yelled Alf angrily.

Alf and Frits began to push each other.
They fell to the ground. The kids
crowded around.

"Stop it!" shouted Doc.

"Ouch!" yelled Alf.

"Quit it. You'll get hurt!" said Hot Rod.

"Yikes!" howled Frits.

The kids had to pull the two boys
apart.

Ettabetta said, "Aw, come on. Cut it out. Let's play tag."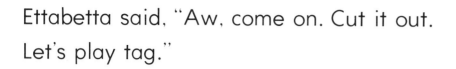

"No! I quit!" said Frits, as he stomped off to the bus. "I am not going to play tag with a cheater."

"I quit, too!" yelled Alf. "Who wants to play with a grouch? I am going home." Alf left in a huff.

The rest of the kids just sat there.

Sal said, "This is no fun. They have spoiled the game for us, too."

"Let's forget about the game!" said Toc. "Let's just go." The kids split up and walked home.

The next day the kids met at the bus.
Frits sat at one end of the bus.
Alf sat at the other end. Both of them
were frowning.

"It is too warm to play tag today,"
Toc said. "I know! Let's go fishing!"

"Hurray!" shouted the kids happily.

Alf said, "Well, I am not going if
Frits goes."

"And I am not going if Alf goes,"
said Frits.

Toc got angry. "You spoiled our game yesterday," she said. "But you are not going to spoil our fishing trip. You can both just stay here! You are not invited. Come on, kids. Let's go!"

The kids got up and walked off the bus. Frits and Alf were left on the bus alone. They had never been left out before.

Alf frowned at Frits.

Frits scowled at Alf.

"The kids don't want us around anymore," said Alf. "Now look what you did."

"What I did?" asked Frits. "How about you? You started this."

"I did not," said Alf.

"You did, too," said Frits.

"Oh, I wish you would just get out of here," grumbled Alf.

"I got here first!" shouted Frits.

"O.K., then stay. I don't care," said Alf. He picked up a comic and began to read it.

Frits just stared out the window.

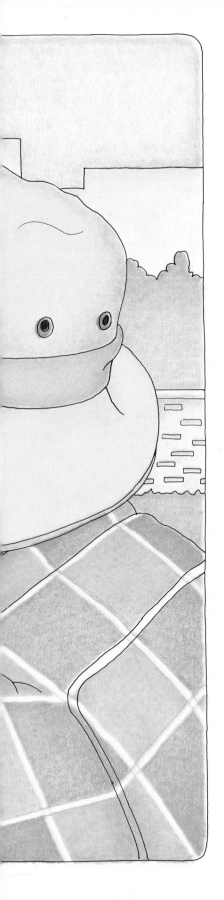

For a long time Frits and Alf sat
on the bus without making a sound.

Then Alf said softly, "Wow!"

Frits asked, "What?"

"Look at this!" said Alf. "This comic
shows you how to make a skateboard!
Isn't that terrific?"

"Let me see!" said Frits. Alf handed
the comic to him. "Yes, that really
is pretty terrific."

"All you need is a board and some
skates," said Alf. "If only I had
some skates!"

Frits said, "I have skates we could
use. Let's walk to my house and get them!"

"O.K.!" said Alf. "Let's go!"

As Frits and Alf were running off the bus, they bumped into Sal. Sal looked surprised.

"Where are you two going?" he asked.

"We are going to get my skates," said Frits.

"We are working on a super project," said Alf.

Sal said, "I didn't think you two were speaking to each other."

Alf looked at Frits. Frits looked at Alf. All at once they began to laugh.

"Well . . . that was yesterday," said Alf.

# Chapter 8
## The Case of the Mystery Monster 144

oo

book               room

books              soon

bookshelf

good

look

looked

took

live    eight    old    hold    write

mystery        library        Mr.

# The Case of the Mystery Monster

Lily took a pile of books to the checkout desk at the library.

"You must like mystery books," Mr. Burns said.

"Oh, yes," Lily said. "I heard a scary story at a slumber party. Now I like to read a good scary story just before I go to bed."

Mr. Burns frowned. "You aren't the only one who likes mystery books!" he said. "Eight new mystery books are missing."

"Who would take the books?" asked Lily.

"Well, I have one clue," Mr. Burns said. "I found this note on the mystery bookshelf."

He handed Lily a scrap of paper that said,

Hold on to your books! The Mystery Monster lives here!

"Monster!" said Lily. "That is silly. How could a monster get in here?"

"I don't know," said Mr. Burns. "It may not be a monster. But someone is writing notes and taking the books."

"Maybe I can help you," Lily said. "I can come every day and look out for the Mystery Monster."

"Well, thank you, Lily," said Mr. Burns. "That would be a big help."

The next day Lily went back to the library. "Hi, Mr. Burns," she said. "Did the Mystery Monster write any more notes?"

"No, not yet," said Mr. Burns. "But after you left yesterday, another book was missing! It was called I Live with a Goblin. If any more books disappear, I may turn into an old monster myself."

"Well," said Lily. "I hope we can catch this
monster before he takes any more books.
I'll sit next to the mystery shelf.
Maybe the monster will come today."

Lily opened her book. She was reading
The Mystery of the Eight Old Lost Bones.

Outside, the sky was turning gray.
Inside the library, the room got dark.
Far down the street a dog howled.
Lily switched on the table light.
Then she settled down to read.

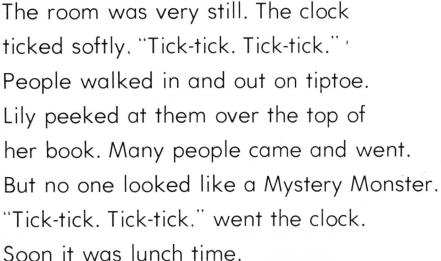

The room was very still. The clock
ticked softly, "Tick-tick. Tick-tick."
People walked in and out on tiptoe.
Lily peeked at them over the top of
her book. Many people came and went.
But no one looked like a Mystery Monster.
"Tick-tick. Tick-tick," went the clock.
Soon it was lunch time.

"Well, I am starved," Lily said to
herself. She closed her book and
started to get up. An old man in a
gray coat bumped into her chair.

"Excuse me," he mumbled. Then he
walked over to the mystery bookshelf.
Lily sat down quickly and looked at
the man. But the man just frowned at
the mystery books. Then he walked on
to the sports books.

"Well, it seems that man isn't
interested in mystery books," Lily said
to herself.

She found Mr. Burns with a big stack of old books on his desk. "Nothing is happening in the mystery department," Lily said to him. "Is it O.K. if I go home for lunch now?"

"Oh, yes," said Mr. Burns. "Even a spy has to eat lunch."

Lily looked at some other books on the mystery shelf. Then she walked back to the table to get her book. But when she got there, her book had disappeared! On the table was a scrap of paper:

Hold on to your books! The Mystery Monster lives here!

Lily whirled around. The man in the gray coat was walking quickly to the exit.

Lily ran over to Mr. Burns. "Mr. Burns!" she whispered. "Stop that man! He took my book. He is the Mystery Monster!"

Mr. Burns looked surprised. He jumped up from his desk. Books went tumbling everywhere. All the library workers ran over to see what was the matter. "Sh!" they said to Mr. Burns. Mr. Burns blushed.

And the man in the gray coat went outside!

"Oh, no," said Lily. "Now we will never catch him. Mr. Burns, the Mystery Monster got away! We must run after him!"

Mr. Burns looked very upset. "Oh, dear. Oh, dear," he said softly to himself. Then he looked at Lily sadly. "Perhaps I let my little joke go too far. Let me show you something, Lily."

Mr. Burns took out a big tube from under his desk. Inside the tube was a big sheet of paper. This is what Lily saw on the paper:

Boys and Girls!
Coming Soon!
Mystery Book Week at the Library!
We'll have a Mystery Book Club and a Mystery Book Corner.
All Mystery Book Fans Invited.
The Mystery Monster

"Wow!" said Lily.

"You see, Lily," said Mr. Burns. "I was going to put this up next week. Mystery Book Week is coming in eight days. I have been holding on to all the mystery books for the Mystery Corner. I put all the books under my desk. I was writing the notes myself."

"Oh, so you are the Mystery Monster," said Lily with a giggle.

"That is right," said Mr. Burns. "But now the surprise is spoiled for all the other boys and girls who live here."

"No, it isn't," said Lily with a smile. "I won't tell about Mystery Book Week. I can keep it to myself. After all, today I tracked down a real mystery myself!"

# Chapter 9
## Zoo Clue 156

give

have

house

live

love

noise

please

solve

tease

I'm     he's     she's     it's     they're     we're     you're

# Zoo Clue

"Where is Ettabetta?" asked Toc. "She asked us to meet her here at the zoo."

"Maybe she's inside," said Cass. "Let's go in and see if we can find her."

The kids went up to the ticket booth.

"Are you the Superkids?" asked the person at the booth.

"Yes, we're the Superkids!" said Icky.

"Good. I have something for you," said the ticket taker. And she handed a note to Icky.

"Read it out loud!" said Lily.

Icky opened the note:

Dear Superkids,
This is an animal riddle game.
Read each clue and figure out
which animal it is about.
Go to that animal and there will
be another riddle for you.
Keep going! Solve all the riddles!
There is a terrific prize at the end.
Good luck!
    Love,
        Ettabetta

"Look!" said Hot Rod. "The first riddle is on the back of the note."

I live in the desert.
I have a hump.
You can ride on my back.
I'm kind of a grump!
Look for me.

"A grump! That sounds like Frits," said Icky.

"It does not!" laughed Frits. "It sounds like a camel!"

"Yes! Let's go look for the camel," said Cass.

The Superkids hunted for the camel. They went past the baboons and the apes. They stopped to look at the seals swimming in a pool. A man was holding a pail of fish. He let Doc feed a slippery fish to a seal. The seal clapped and made a lot of noise. At last the kids found the camel.

"Wow! Look at the funny shape of the camel's hump," laughed Hot Rod. The camel shook and snorted.

"I don't think that old camel liked that too much!" said Doc. "He's a grouch!"

"Look, there is another note," said Hot Rod.
"What did Ettabetta write this time?"
He took down the note. Here is what
it said:

I give milk,
And I say "moo."
I live on a farm,
But I'm here at the zoo.
Look for me.

"That is a goat!" said Oswald.
"I know that goats give milk."

"But goats don't moo," said Lily.
"Cows moo!"

"That is true," said Oswald. "Let's find
the cow."

When the kids went to look for the cow, they went past a goat. There was a little goat standing next to it.

"Oh, look at that cute little goat," said Tac.

"It's super!" said Sal.

"A little goat is called a kid," said Oswald.

"Then that little goat is a superkid!" said Sal.

All the kids laughed.

At last they came to the cow.
"Moo," said the cow.

"Moo to you, too," said Cass.

"Look, there is another note!"
said Oswald.

Cass said, "Read it!"

I have two big ears
And a coat of brown.
I fly when it is dark,
And I hang upside down.
Look for me.

162

"What is a coat of brown?" asked Tac. "Does this animal dress up in a coat?"

"No, a coat of brown means its fur is brown," said Oswald.

"Well, if it has two big ears and brown fur, this animal could be a rabbit," said Tic.

"But rabbits don't fly," said Tac. "It must be a bird. Let's go to the bird house."

"But birds don't have big ears," said Toc.

"It could be an owl! Owls look like they have ears. And they fly!" said Tac.

"But owls never hang upside down," said Icky. "Hold it! I know! It's a bat."

"That fits!" said Oswald. "Let's go!"

The kids ran past two kangaroos and
a peacock and a cockatoo. They didn't stop.
At last they came to the bat house.
Inside the bat house, it was as dark
as a cave. Seven or eight bats were
flying around.

"Oh, they're scary. I don't like it in here.
Let's go!" said Cass.

"Well, bats have to live in the dark,"
said Oswald. "Wait a second!
Here is another note."

"She's left another note?" said Hot Rod.
"What did Ettabetta write this time?"

The kids took the note outside
to read it. It said:

This note is not a clue.
If you go to the petting zoo,
There will be a prize for you.
Ettabetta will be there, too.

"A prize!" said Hot Rod. "Let's go get it!"

"O.K.!" yelled the kids. They ran to the
petting zoo. Ettabetta was sitting on
a bench.

"Hi, Ettabetta!" shouted all the kids.

"Where have you been? You're late!"
said Ettabetta. "I was about to give up
on you!"

"Well, we had a hard time with your
riddles," said Alf.

"We stopped to look at the animals,"
said Toc.

I live in the desert.
I have a hump.
You can ride on my back.
I'm kind of a grump!
Look for me.

I give milk,
And I say "moo".
I live on a farm,
But I'm here at the zoo.
Look for me.

I have two big ears
And a coat of brown.
I fly when it is dark,
And I hang upside down.
Look for me.

This note is not a clue.
If you go to the petting zoo,
There will be a prize for you.
Ettabetta will be there, too.

"Where is our prize?" asked Icky.

"You'll have to figure out what the
prize is first," said Ettabetta.

"Oh, please, Ettabetta! Don't tease
us! I am getting tired," said Sal.

"Hold up all the clues together,"
said Ettabetta. "Then look at the
red letters in the clues. Put them
together to make a word. The word
will tell you what the prize is."

166

The kids held up the clues and looked at the red letters.

167

"I have it!" said Sal.
"It's ZOO BALLOONS!"